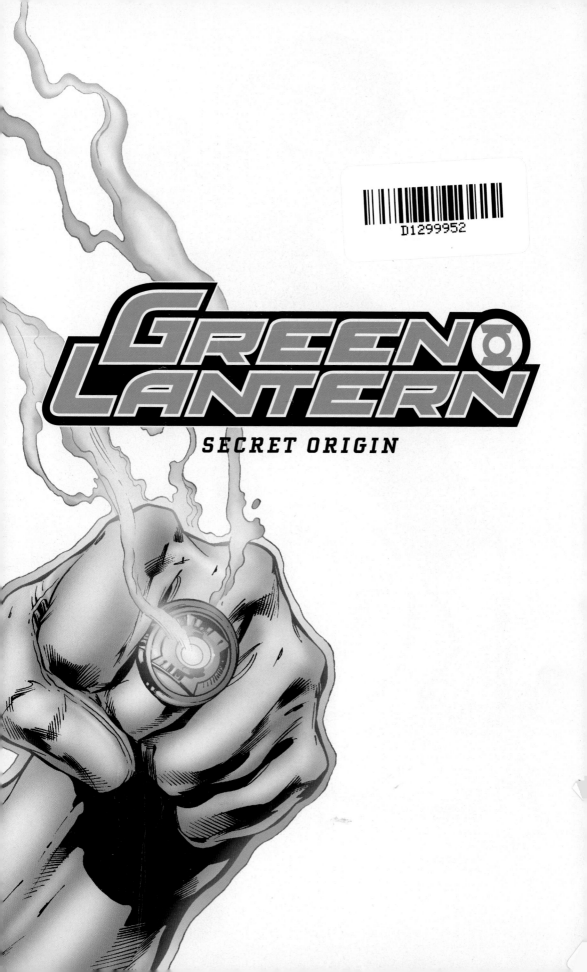

Green Lantern

SECRET ORIGIN

Green Lantern

SECRET ORIGIN

Geoff Johns
Writer

Ivan Reis
Penciller

Oclair Albert
Inker

Randy Mayor
Colors

Rob Leigh
Letters

With
Julio Ferreira Partial Inker Book 3
Ivan Reis Partial Inker Book 6

Original Series Covers by **Ivan Reis** and **Dave McCaig**

DC COMICS

Dan DiDio Senior VP-Executive Editor
Eddie Berganza Editor-original series
Adam Schlagman Assistant Editor-original series
Bob Joy Editor-collected edition
Robbin Brosterman Senior Art Director
Paul Levitz President & Publisher
Georg Brewer VP-Design & DC Direct Creative
Richard Bruning Senior VP-Creative Director
Patrick Caldon Executive VP-Finance & Operations
Chris Caramalis VP-Finance
John Cunningham VP-Marketing
Terri Cunningham VP-Managing Editor
Amy Genkins Senior VP-Business & Legal Affairs
Alison Gill VP-Manufacturing
David Hyde VP-Publicity
Hank Kanalz VP-General Manager, WildStorm
Jim Lee Editorial Director-WildStorm
Gregory Noveck Senior VP-Creative Affairs
Sue Pohja VP-Book Trade Sales
Steve Rotterdam Senior VP-Sales & Marketing
Cheryl Rubin Senior VP-Brand Management
Alysse Soll VP-Advertising & Custom Publishing
Jeff Trojan VP-Business Development, DC Direct
Bob Wayne VP-Sales

Cover art by Ivan Reis and Dave McCaig

**GREEN LANTERN: SECRET ORIGIN
(SUBMLASTIC EDITION)**

Published by DC Comics. Cover and compilation
Copyright © 2010 DC Comics. All Rights Reserved.

Originally published in single magazine form in
GREEN LANTERN 29-35 Copyright © 2008
DC Comics. All Rights Reserved. All characters,
their distinctive likenesses and related elements
featured in this publication are trademarks of
DC Comics. The stories, characters and incidents
featured in this publication are entirely fictional.
DC Comics does not read or accept unsolicited
submissions of ideas, stories or artwork.

DC Comics, 1700 Broadway, New York, NY 10019
A Warner Bros. Entertainment Company
Printed in the USA. First Printing.

ISBN: 978-1-4012-3192-7

"WHAT ARE YOU AFRAID OF?"

PEOPLE LIKE TO ASK ME THAT. WHEN THEY DO, THEY HAVE THIS KNOWING GRIN ON THEIR FACES. AS IF THEY EXPECT ME TO ANSWER, "NOTHING."

I HUMOR THEM MOST OF THE TIME, BECAUSE THAT'S WHAT THEY WANT ME TO SAY.

"I'M NOT AFRAID OF ANYTHING."

THEY THINK I WAS BORN WITHOUT FEAR.

THEY'RE WRONG.

THEY THINK THIS RING GIVES ME THE POWER TO DO ANYTHING.

THEY'RE WRONG ABOUT THAT TOO.

BEFORE I WAS GIVEN THE GREATEST WEAPON IN THE UNIVERSE, BEFORE I JOURNEYED TO THE STARS--

--MY DAD GAVE ME THE POWER TO DO ANYTHING.

HE TOLD ME I COULD BE WHATEVER I WANTED TO BE.

I'M HAVING SOME *PROBLEMS* HERE, FERRIS. OIL'S GETTIN' EATEN UP *QUICK*. I THINK THE LAST OF MY TORQUE PINS JUST FAILED.

I THOUGHT THIS WAS SENT TO I-LEVEL *REPAIR.*

IT *WAS.*

DADDY!

DADDY, THAT BOY IS BREAKING THE *RULES!*

ONE MINUTE, HONEY, OKAY?

I NEED TO BRING IT IN. *AWAY* FROM THE CROWD.

THERE'S NO EXTERNAL LEAKAGE. THE INVESTORS ARE *WATCHING.*

THAT'S *FIFTEEN-MILLION DOLLARS* AND OUR LAST *SIX YEARS* OF *DEVELOPMENT* YOU HAVE IN THE *AIR.*

KEEP IT *FLYING,* JORDAN.

THIS THING'S GOING *DOWN,* FERRIS.

ON TOP OF YOU, COAST CITY, OR RIGHT *HERE...*

...AND RIGHT *HERE* NO ONE ELSE GETS HURT.

WHEN YOUR WORST FEAR HAPPENS IN FRONT OF YOUR EYES--

DAD.

--I THOUGHT THERE WAS NOTHING *LEFT* TO BE AFRAID OF.

MOM THOUGHT THERE WAS *EVERYTHING.*

I'M SO *SORRY,* KEN.

IT'S OKAY, JESSICA...

...HE'S JUST GOT A LOT OF HIS FATHER IN HIM.

HOW MANY *TIMES* HAVE YOU *PROMISED* ME YOU WOULDN'T GO TO THE AIRFIELDS, HAL?

YOU SAID *FERRIS AIR.*

YOU ARE NOT ALLOWED *ANYWHERE* NEAR A PLANE, DO YOU UNDERSTAND ME, YOUNG MAN?

DO YOU?

YES, MA'AM.

I DIDN'T UNDERSTAND HER.

AND SHE DIDN'T UNDERSTAND ME.

SON?

CAN I HELP YOU?

I'M EIGHTEEN TODAY, SIR.

COAST CITY WAS LESS THAN HALF AN HOUR FROM EDWARDS. TWENTY MINUTES FROM FORT ROCK.

AND THERE WAS ALWAYS A BATTLESHIP OR THREE IN THE HARBOR.

COAST CITY WAS A MILITARY TOWN.

AND FRIDAY NIGHT, IT ALWAYS LIT UP LIKE A ROCKET. THAT NIGHT, IT WAS PACKED BY THE AIR FORCE AND THE MARINES, READY FOR TAKE OFF.

...YOU'RE THE *BEST SHOT* IN THE CORPS. WE'D *HATE* TO LOSE YOU.

...YOU'RE *SCREWED*, HIGHBALL. YOU PISSED OFF STONE. YOU *INVALIDATED* HIS ENTIRE *TWO-YEAR* PROGRAM.

I SAVED THE AIR FORCE *TWO YEARS* OF TEST FLIGHTS. THE F-16'S READY FOR COMBAT *NOW*, ROCKET-MAN.

YOU *DESTROYED* A THIRTY MILLION DOLLAR *JET* TO PROVE THAT?

IF THAT'S WHAT IT TAKES TO GET OUR PILOTS IN THE *SAFEST* EQUIPMENT *SOONER* THAN *LATER*, FINE.

STONE'S GONNA TAKE THIS OUT ON *ALL* OF US.

THAT'S WHY THE *DRINKS* ARE ON *ME*.

LET *GO*.

YOU'RE COMING *HOME* WITH *ME*, CINDY.

NO, I'M *NOT*.

I'M NOT GOING *ANYWHERE*!

YOU'RE COMING NOW OR I'LL *SNAP* YOUR NECK.

HEY, WARTHOG. THE LADY DOESN'T WANT TO GO WITH YOU.

MIND YOUR OWN BUSINESS, FLYBOY.

THAT HURTS--

--OWW!

YOU SEE THAT, STEWART? THAT *JET JOCKEY* JUST KNOCKED DOWN ONE OF *OURS.*

HERE WE GO.

HERE WE GO.

--WHEN IT COMES TO *WAR,* WE MIGHT ALL BE ON THE SAME SIDE. BUT IF YOU THINK THERE'S NO INTERSERVICE RIVALRY BETWEEN THE AMERICAN ARMED FORCES--

--YOU'RE AS SHARP AS A *JARHEAD.*

YOU SHOULD BE *HAPPY.*

THIS IS MORE *FIGHTING* THAN THE AIR FORCE WILL SHOW YOU ALL YEAR.

THEN I BETTER MAKE IT *COUNT.*

HAL?

JIM?

IT'S PAST *TWO* IN THE MORNING. WHAT ARE YOU DOING--?

I KNOW THIS IS YOUR HANGOUT. I'VE BEEN WAITING FOR YOU. LIKE ALWAYS.

BRO, I--

MOM'S DYING.

WHAT IS IT?

CANCER. IT STARTED IN THE PANCREAS. AND IT'S *BAD.*

I NEED TO SEE HER.

YOU *CAN'T.*

WHAT DO YOU MEAN I CAN'T?

YOU KNOW WHAT MOM SAID. AS LONG AS YOU'RE IN THE AIR FORCE--

THIS IS *DIFFERENT,* JIM.

THE DOCTORS SAID THE STATE SHE'S IN, ANYTHING *UPSETTING* COULD TRIGGER ALL SORTS OF *PHYSICAL* PROBLEMS.

JACK WON'T LET YOU.

I CAN'T LET YOU EITHER.

THE NEXT MORNING, I GOT TO BASE EARLY. INSTEAD OF REPORTING RIGHT TO STONE'S OFFICE, I TOOK AN UNAUTHORIZED JOYRIDE.

...THE LAST TIME THE AIR FORCE LOST THIS MANY JETS IN *ONE WEEK* WE WERE AT WAR IN *VIETNAM*.

NOW I'VE GOT TO CALL THE PENTAGON AND EXPLAIN HOW WE LOST A THIRTY MILLION DOLLAR FIGHTER ON A DAMN *TEST FLIGHT* TO DETERMINE...

..."STRUCTURAL LIMITATIONS OF THE F-16 AT MACH ONE." THIS WASN'T EVEN A *COMBAT* SIMULATION!

IT WAS THE FIRST TIME I DIDN'T SMILE IN THE AIR.

WHEN I LANDED, STONE WAS WAITING FOR ME.

YOU MAY BE THE "*BEST*" PILOT ON *PAPER*, BUT IN *REALITY* YOU'RE THE MOST *EXPENSIVE* AND THE *MOST DANGEROUS*.

IT'S TIME YOU USE THAT *LUMP* ON YOUR SHOULDERS ONCE IN AWHILE.

STONE'S WORDS WERE JUST A FOG AROUND ME. LIKE JACK'S.

BUT I ALWAYS LISTENED TO JIM. AND THAT'S ALL I WAS HEARING.

"MOM'S DYING."

I JUST TOOK HER FOR A SPIN, MAJOR.

WITHOUT CLEARANCE AND WITHOUT AUTHORIZATION, JOYRIDING LIKE IT WAS YOUR *LAST* FLIGHT.

IT WAS. I KNEW IT WAS.

I COULDN'T SAY IT. I COULDN'T WALK AWAY. I COULDN'T QUIT.

I HAD TO FIND ANOTHER WAY OUT.

ANOTHER BAD CHOICE IN A LIFE FULL OF THEM.

HAL? HOW DID YOU...?

I CAME TO SEE MOM. YOU CAN TELL HER I WAS DISCHARGED, JIM. I'M *OUT* OF THE AIR FORCE.

YOU CAN TELL HER I KEPT MY PROMISE.

HAL, THERE WAS A COMPLICATION THIS AFTERNOON...

...MOM'S *GONE*.

WHAT? WHAT HAPPENED?

YOU KILLED HER.

JACK?

AFTER YOU *RAN AWAY*, SHE SPENT HER *LIFE* WORRYING.

SHE *HEARD* ABOUT ALL THE *CLOSE CALLS*. ALL THE *CRASHES*.

YOU KILLED MOM!

JACK! THIS IS TOUGH FOR *ALL* OF US--

SINCE WHEN IS *ANYTHING* TOUGH FOR HAL, JIM? WHEN DAD DIED *I* TOOK CARE OF MOM. I GOT A JOB TO HELP.

WHEN HAL RAN AWAY I LEFT COLLEGE. I MOVED HOME.

I GAVE MY *LIFE* FOR OUR FAMILY JUST LIKE MOM.

I WAS DAD'S SON. JIM WAS MOM'S. JACK WAS ALWAYS ON HIS OWN PATH...

WHEN HAS HAL *EVER* GIVEN THIS FAMILY *ANYTHING?*

...BUT I TOOK HIM OFF IT.

I WAS NEVER A GOOD BROTHER TO ANYONE.

NOK NOK

GLASS

JIM? COME ON IN--

I CAN'T.

SUSAN'S WAITING IN THE CAR.

TO MY Brother HAL

WHAT'S THIS?

SOMETHING I WISH I COULD'VE GIVEN YOU A LONG TIME AGO.

I THOUGHT NO ONE UNDERSTOOD ME.

I WAS WRONG.

TO MY Brother HAL

I'D BEEN DISHONORABLY DISCHARGED. I TORE MY FAMILY APART.

I STARED AT THAT PICTURE OF ME AND DAD ALL NIGHT. WONDERING...

...WHERE DO I GO FROM HERE?

THERE IS NO ESCAPE.

THAT IS WHY I HAVE RETURNED TO THIS FESTERING PIT OF A PLANET, QULL. I CAN HEAR THE SADISTIC LAUGHTER YOU DEMONS SHARE OVER THE HORROR THAT APPROACHES OTHERS.

I WILL STOP THAT HORROR. I WANT TO KNOW MORE ABOUT THE PROPHECIES YOU HAVE SEEN.

YOU KNOW THAT, DON'T YOU, ABIN SUR? YOU BELIEVE OUR PROPHECIES.

QUIET, QULL! YOU HAVE TOLD ABIN SUR ENOUGH!

THOSE SECRETS REMAIN WITH US, GREEN LANTERN!

I HAVE HAD ENOUGH, ATRORCITUS!

YOU DO NOT GET TO CHOOSE WHEN YOU TALK TO ME AND WHEN YOU DO NOT.

AAARRG!

I WILL KNOW EVERYTHING YOU KNOW, DEMONS. ABOUT THE FATE OF THE UNIVERSE. ABOUT COSMIC REVELATIONS.

AND ABOUT "THE BLACKEST NIGHT."

DON'T LET LAMINSKI GET TO YOU, HAL.

...HAL? WHAT'RE YOU STARIN' AT?

THAT PLANE.

YEAH. TRASH HEAP'S SEEN BETTER DAYS. NOT GOOD FOR ANYTHIN' BUT PARTS.

I REMEMBER IT.

YOU REMEMBER IT?

MY DAD FLEW FOR A LOT OF AIRFIELDS IN COAST CITY. HE TOOK ME UP WITH HIM IN THAT PLANE ONCE.

LONG TIME AGO.

"DAD. I'M SCARED."

DON'T WORRY. YOU'RE FLYING WITH *ME*, SON.

YOU'VE NEVER FLOWN WITH *ME*.

I NEED TO GET BACK IN THE AIR.

ARTIN "BISHOP" JORDAN. KEN "HIGH LIFE" ARDEN.
ONATHAN "HERC" STONE. CARL "ROOK" FERRIS.

EY CALLED THEMSELVES THE
UR MUSKETEERS WHEN THEY WERE
THE AIR FORCE. EVENTUALLY, ALL
F THEM EXCEPT STONE LEFT TO
ORK IN THE PRIVATE SECTOR.

D BEEN SNEAKING ONTO
RDEN'S AIRFIELD SINCE
WAS A KID.

THAT'S WHY HE CUT
ME A BREAK WITH A
JOB. HE KNEW DAD.
HE KNEW MOM.

HE KNEW ME.

NO.

BUT I'M *TEN TIMES* THE PILOT LAMINSKI IS.

YOU'RE ALSO *TEN TIMES* AS DANGEROUS. THE PLANES YOU BROUGHT DOWN IN THE AIR FORCE DIDN'T *VANISH* OFF YOUR RECORD.

MAYBE I PUSHED IT A LITTLE. I WON'T--

PUTTING YOU BACK IN THE AIR ISN'T UP TO ME.

ONE FLIGHT.

I *SAID* IT'S NOT UP TO ME.

LOOK, I'M GETTING OLD. BUSINESS HASN'T BEEN GREAT...

...I GOT AN OFFER I COULDN'T REFUSE LAST WEEK.

I'M *SELLING* TO FERRIS AIR.

FERRIS?! YOU CAN'T BE SERIOUS.

AFTER WHAT HE *DID*... HOW COULD YOU SELL TO FERRIS?

MR. ARDEN?

I HAVE THE FINAL PAPERS. MY FATHER WOULD HAVE BROUGHT THEM HIMSELF, BUT APPARENTLY HE'S GOLFING THE GAME OF HIS *LIFE* IN PEBBLE BEACH.

IT'S *NICE* HE CAN ENJOY HIS GOLDEN YEARS.

CAROL. THIS IS HAL--

JORDAN. OF COURSE. IT'S BEEN A LONG TIME.

CAROL'S FATHER RETIRED A FEW YEARS AGO. SHE'S COME OUT OF THE COCKPIT TO RUN FERRIS AIR.

YOU'RE A PILOT?

I *WAS.* I HAVE MORE IMPORTANT THINGS TO DO.

LIKE *NOW,* MR. JORDAN.

HE'S A PROBLEM.

THE DEAL WAS YOU KEEP HIM ON.

MY FATHER'S NOT GOING TO LIKE THIS.

...DAD.

...AND I FEEL *FREEDOM!*

THE IRONY OF IT ALL. IN THE MOMENT OF DEATH, YOUR RING DID NOT FAIL *YOU,* LANTERN.

YOU FAILED *IT.*

GSHNNK

N-NO.

AAARRR!

~KAFF~

...RING. PREPARE MESSAGE AND FILE INFORMATION FOR SINESTRO. HE MUST CONTINUE MY MISSION. IT IS NOT ONE FOR A ROOKIE...NNN...

SPACE SECTOR SCAN 2814 FOR REPLACEMENT SENTIENT INITIATED.

HAL JORDAN.

WHAT--?

YOU HAVE BEEN CHOSEN.

BOOOMMMM

WHAT--?

GREEN LIGHT GRAFTED OVER MY BODY. IT WAS HOT.

WOOOSHH

BUT THE BLACK WAS AS COLD AS ICE.

I NEED SOME AIR. GOTTA GET OUT.

WILLPOWER RECOGNIZED. RING ONLINE.

WHO IS THAT? WHO'S TALK--?

ORDERS ACCEPTED.

IS THAT THE RING?

AFFIRMATIVE.

BOOOMMM

HOLY #?$%!

HOLY #?$%!

HOLY #?$%!

THERE WAS NO RUMBLING OF ANY ENGINE.

NO STICK TO PULL ON.

NO TOWER TO GET PERMISSION FROM.

IT WAS JUST ME.

ME AND THE RING.

BOOOOMM

HA HA HA HA HA HA HA HA HA

...YOU ARE CLEAR TO OPEN ENGINE FOUR, LAMINSKI.

LAMINSKI? DO YOU COPY?

YEAH, YEAH. I COPY THAT, TOWER.

YOU HEARD THE NEWS, RIGHT? FERRIS AIR BOUGHT ARDEN OUT. CARL FERRIS--

CARL FERRIS HAS BEEN RETIRED FOR YEARS. HE'S GOT THAT SWEET LITTLE *DAUGHTER* RUNNING HIS AIRFIELDS.

WITHIN A WEEK, I'LL BE TEACHIN' HER A NEW MEANING FOR THE TERM...

LAMINSKI? LAMINSKI, WHAT WAS THAT?

I... I DON'T...

TEN TIMES THE PILOT.

YOU'RE LOSING CONTROL! LAMINSKI?!

LOSE YOUR COOL AT FIFTEEN THOUSAND FEET--

--PAY THE PRICE. C'MON, LAMINSKI.

STEADY.

STEADY NOW.

WHAT THE HECK HAPPENED, TOM?

I SAW SOMETHING GLOWING, MR. ARDEN. SOMETHING *GREEN*.

OW.

SENTIENTS APPROACHING.

CONCEALING IDENTITY.

Hnn.

STOP *DOING* THAT.

WHOA.

_Um. Hi._

YOUR PILOT MIGHT, _uh_, NEED SOME MEDICAL ATTENTION. I THINK I HEARD HIM THROW UP.

WHO THE HECK ARE YOU?

GREEN LANTERN OF SPACE SECTOR 2814.

GREEN... LANTERN?

WHAT'S A "GREEN LANTERN"?

KLUK

I'M CURIOUS WHAT A "GREEN LANTERN" IS _MYSELF_, CAROL.

YOU'RE NOT TRYING TO STEAL MY GIRL, ARE YOU, SUPER-HERO?

CAROL HADN'T LOOKED UP FROM HER ACCOUNTING BOOKS IN YEARS.

SHE'D FORGOTTEN WHY SHE EVER DID.

Ah-HEM.

A LIFE TURNED UPSIDE DOWN.

I'M SURE MISS FERRIS APPRECIATES THE CATCH, BUT YOU CAN LET GO OF HER NOW.

RIGHT.

RIGHT.

A DYING ALIEN.

A WISHING RING.

THE GLOW OF THE UNIFORM KEPT THEM BLINDED ENOUGH. THEY DIDN'T RECOGNIZE ME BEHIND THE MASK.

AT LEAST, MOST OF THEM.

WHERE'D THOSE GIANT GREEN HANDS THAT WERE HOLDING THE PLANE GO? HOW'D YOU DO THAT?

CONSTRUCT MANIFESTATION TRIGGERED BY FORCE OF WILL.

WILL YOU SHUT UP?!

SILENT MODE ACTIVATED.

YOU ACT AS IF YOU BARELY KNOW WHAT'S HAPPENING YOURSELF.

I'M A SCIENTIST. I SPECIALIZE IN ASTROPHYSICS, ALTERNATIVE FUEL SOURCES AND THEORETICAL FUTURE-SCIENCE.

PERHAPS I CAN BE OF ASSISTANCE.

TRUTHFULLY, I DIDN'T KNOW WHAT I WAS DOING.

BUT I'D FIGURE IT OUT MYSELF.

NO, THANKS.

THAT'S WHAT I ALWAYS DID.

WHO IS HE?

WHERE'D HE COME FROM?

ARE YOU ALL RIGHT, CAROL?

CAROL.

I APPRECIATE YOUR CONCERN, DR. HAMMOND, BUT *ONE* DINNER DOES NOT MAKE ME "YOUR GIRL."

YOU'RE AN *EMPLOYEE.*

AND I'VE MADE IT CRYSTAL CLEAR. I DON'T *DATE* EMPLOYEES.

I'M *NOT* AN EMPLOYEE. I'M A *CONSULTANT.*

YOU CAN'T TREAT ME LIKE YOU DO *EVERYONE ELSE.* FERRIS AIR ISN'T THE *ONLY* COMPANY I WORK--

VEENEET

TELL YOUR FATHER "HELLO."

WHO WAS HE?

I ASKED THE SAME QUESTIONS EVERYONE AT FERRIS DID.

ABOUT THIS ALIEN.

HE WAS OBVIOUSLY SOME KIND OF SOLDIER OR OFFICER.

I WASN'T GOING TO LEAVE HIM OUT IN THE OPEN.

HE DESERVED BETTER THAN THAT.

NO MATTER WHO HE WAS.

THE GREEN LANTERN? IS THAT WHAT *THIS* IS?

RING? RING, YOU CAN *TALK* NOW.

THIS IS YOUR POWER BATTERY.

POWER BATTERY? WHAT'S A POWER BATTER--

HEY!

A GREEN LANTERN'S POWER BATTERY IS THEIR POWER RING'S CHARGING STATION. RECHARGING REQUIRED APPROXIMATELY EVERY TWENTY-FOUR TERRESTRIAL HOURS.

LET GO!

INCORRECT OATH.

KLANK

POWER LEVELS 100%.

GREEN LANTERN OF SPACE SECTOR 2814.

YOU WILL REPORT TO OA FOR TRAINING IMMEDIATELY.

WHAT?

HAVE A NICE FLIGHT.

BOOOM

DESCENDING FROM HYPERSPACE.

UNIVERSAL TRANSLATOR ON.

HEY!

WHERE AM I?

THE PLANET OA. CENTRAL PRECINCT OF THE GREEN LANTERN CORPS.

AND HOME TO THE GUARDIANS OF THE UNIVERSE-- IMMORTAL WATCHERS AND PROTECTORS OF ALL.

ABIN?

DISENGAGING AUTOPILOT.

WAIT. WHY DID YOU BRING ME HERE?

WHAT AM I SUPPOSED TO DO NOW?

HELLO?!

TUTORIAL OFF.

SPLAATT!

HAHAHAHAHAHAHAH

IS THAT A HUMAN?

A HUMAN GREEN LANTERN?

WHAT'S A HUMAN?

THAT'S NO WAY TA TREAT YOUR BATTERY.

NICE LANDIN', POOZER.

NAME'S KILOWOG.

WELCOME TA RINGSLINGIN' 101. OR AS KE'HAAN AND I LIKE TA CALL IT--

--THE WORST DAY A' YOUR WORTHLESS LIFE!

OH, I GET IT.

THIS IS BOOT CAMP.

GET IN LINE WITH THE REST OF THE WHITE CIRCLES.

IT'S WHERE YOU PRIMORDIAL QUADRUPEDS BELONG.

YOU WANNA BOX?

LET'S BOX.

YOU REALLY SHOULDN'T HAVE DONE THAT.

WHY NOT?

BECAUSE I'VE BEEN LOOKIN' *ALL DAY* FOR SOMEBODY TA MAKE AN *EXAMPLE* OUTTA!

THEY WERE TRACKING IT WHEN IT FLEW PAST MARS.

BUT IT WASN'T UNTIL IT *TURNED* TOWARD EARTH THAT IT WAS RED FLAGGED.

SOMETHING BROKE OFF WHEN IT ENTERED THE ATMOSPHERE. RIGHT ABOVE BIG BEAR, CALIFORNIA.

FORT ROCK'S SENT A UNIT TO INVESTIGATE THE SECOND CRASH SITE. WE'RE HANDLING THIS ONE.

WHAT IS IT, MAJOR STONE? A FALLEN SPY SATELLITE? A METEOR?

YOU'RE THE SCIENTIST THAT SPECIALIZES IN THE THEORETICAL, DR. HAMMOND.

YOU TELL US.

MY GOD...

"...WE'RE NOT ALONE."

SOMETHING LANDED HERE.

LOOKS LIKE IT SLID INTO THE WATER.

WE MIGHT NEED SOME S.E.A.L.S TO...HEY.

YOU GUYS SEE THAT? THE WATER'S *BOILING.*

BLIP

RRAAAARRRR!

DEATH WILL CLAIM YOU. YOU AND ALL THAT THE GREEN LANTERN CORPS RULE OVER.

SO SWEAR THE *SURVIVORS* OF SECTOR 666.

THE RING CAN MAKE WHATEVER **TOOL** YA NEED. JUST GOTTA PICTURE IT IN YOUR MIND. **WILL** IT TO **LIFE**.

FORCE FIELDS. ENERGY BEAMS.

EVERYONE SEE THAT?

YES, **SIR**.

YOU PRACTICE **WELL**, AHTIER. WHY DO YOU SPEAK SO **LITTLE**?

BECAUSE I **FEAR** MY **DUTY**, KE'HAAN.

GREEN LANTERNS BURN **BRIGHT**, BUT THEY BURN OUT **QUICKLY**.

IF THAT **HUMAN** CAN MAKE IT, SO CAN **YOU**.

THANKS FOR THE RIDE, BUT I'LL GET OFF HERE.

KRSHH

YOU **WILLED** YOURSELF FREE, EARTHMAN...

HE DON'T KNOW NOTHIN' 'BOUT THE CORPS, CH'P. HE'S FROM *EARTH.*

ASK ME, KILOWOG, EARTH'S A BACKWARD WORLD BEST LEFT TO THEIR *OWN.*

WHY *YELLOW?*

WHAT?

WHY WOULD THESE RINGS NOT BE ABLE TO AFFECT ANYTHING *YELLOW?*

YOU DON'T ASK QUESTIONS IN THE CORPS. YOU DO YOUR *DUTY.*

I DON'T EVEN KNOW WHAT THAT "*DUTY*" IS.

"TO SERVE AND PROTECT YOUR RESPECTIVE SECTORS AND ALL LIFE WITHIN THEM."

NOW DON'T GET ALL *PUFFY CHESTED* AGAIN. NEXT TIME, I WON'T BE SO NICE.

KILOWOG.

LET ME SPEAK WITH THE EARTHMAN.

WHAT BUSINESS IS HE OF YOURS, TOMAR?

HE'S WEARING *ABIN SUR'S* RING.

MY NAME IS *TOMAR-RE* OF XUDAR. GREEN LANTERN OF SPACE SECTOR 2815.

BY ALL ACCOUNTS, I AM YOUR *NEIGHBOR*.

I'M HAL JORDAN.

ABIN SUR'S REPLACEMENT IN THE CORPS. MY RING IS UNABLE TO *UNLOCK* HIS LOG...HOW DID HE DIE?

HE CRASHED HIS SHIP IN THE DESERT.

HIS *SHIP?*

HE DIDN'T *NEED* THAT SHIP.

THEN WHY WAS HE FLYING ONE?

HE DID WHAT NO GREEN LANTERN SHOULD. HE ALLOWED HIMSELF TO FEEL *FEAR*.

AND IT HAPPENED BECAUSE ABIN SUR DISOBEYED THE GUARDIAN'S TERRITORIAL EDICT AND PURSUED AN ENEMY *OUTSIDE* OF HIS SECTOR.

HE CAME INTO CONFLICT WITH A GROUP KNOWN AS THE EMPIRE OF TEARS.

AFTERWARD, HE GREW INCREASINGLY *PARANOID*.

HE BECAME *OBSESSED* WITH *DOOMSDAY PROPHECIES* AND *PRISMS*.

FRACTURED LIGHT. SPLINTERED SOULS. NOTHING MADE SENSE.

NOTHING MAKES SENSE TO ME RIGHT NOW.

THIS IS THE *BOOK* OF *OA*. IN IT-- TALES OF THE GREEN LANTERN CORPS.

ABIN SUR'S TALE IS NOW AMONG THEM. AN ENDING *TRAGIC.*

ONE DAY *YOUR* TALE WILL BE HERE TOO, AS WILL MINE.

A WORD OF ADVICE, SUCCESSOR.

IF YOU NEED HELP--

--ASK FOR IT.

THE SUN NEVER SET.

YER SUPPOSED TA FLY *AROUND* THEM, JORDAN, NOT *THROUGH* THEM!

I DIDN'T KNOW HOW LONG I GOT MY ASS HANDED TO ME.

I'LL DO IT.

YOU WON'T DO IT.

IT'S JUST A *COLOR*.

DAYS.

YOU MISHANDLE YOUR POWER BATTERY AGAIN, HAL JORDAN, AND SHORM WILL MISHANDLE *YOU*.

UNDERSTOOD, SALAAK.

YOU STILL GOT *CRACKS* IN YOUR CONSTRUCTS, JORDAN--

--BUT IT AIN'T BAD.

A WEEK?

AS CHARGING MY POWER
G ON AN ALIEN WORLD.
DUATING FROM AN
ERGALACTIC BOOT CAMP.

AS SOON AS I WAS DONE, I WAS COVERED IN GREEN LIGHT. I WAS TOLD MY RING WOULD ALERT ME TO ANY EXTRATERRESTRIAL INCIDENTS I SHOULD INTERVENE IN.

THEN I WAS SHIPPED BACK HOME.

HAL?

TOM?

I CAN'T BELIEVE IT! YOU'RE THE *GREEN LANTERN!*

ANY LIFE OUTSIDE THE CORPS WASN'T TAKEN INTO CONSIDERATION.

THE...GREEN LANTERN?

WHAT ARE YOU, *uh,* TALKING ABOUT?

WELL, YOU'RE WEARING A GLOWING GREEN *RING.*

AND THERE'S *THIS.*

WHAT DO YOU MEAN YOU'RE NOT A SUPER-HERO? YOU *CAUGHT* LAMINSKI'S PLANE LAST WEEK!

ANYONE ELSE WOULD'VE DONE THE SAME IF THEY *COULD*.

EVEN IF HE *IS* A JERK.

WELL, YOU'RE NOT GONNA HAVE TO WORRY ABOUT *HIM* ANYMORE.

I'M NOT SUPPOSED TO USE THE RING TO SORT OUT *PERSONAL PROBLEMS*, TOM.

NO, I MEAN THE *WALKOUT*.

WHAT WALKOUT?

KLANG

SEE ALL THE *EMPTY* LOCKERS?

ONCE WORD SPREAD THAT CAROL "LADY" FERRIS WAS TAKING THE REINS FROM MR. ARDEN, NO ONE WAS PARTICULARLY *EXCITED*.

AND AFTER HER FATHER DIDN'T SHOW FOR THE BIG *COMPANY SPEECH*, SHE HAD TO GIVE IT HERSELF--

--AFTERWARDS JUST ABOUT EVERYONE *QUIT*.

...OF COURSE, I'D MAKE IT WORTH YOUR TIME, MR. TRAINOR. PLENTY OF PAY AND BENEFITS AND A SHARE IN THE PROFITS...

...IF YOU KNOW OF ANY OTHER *PILOTS* THAT YOU'D LIKE FLYING ALONGSIDE YOU...

MY FATHER'S STILL TRAVELING. HE'LL BE OUT OF THE COUNTRY THE REST OF THE...

YES, OF COURSE, HE WOULD'VE MADE THE CALL HIMSELF IF HE COULD, BUT...

MR. TRAINOR, LISTEN TO ME. THIS IS THE OPPORTUNITY OF A... MR. TRAINOR?

...LARRY?

NOK NOK

YES?

MISS FERRIS.

MR. JORDAN? WHAT ARE YOU DOING HERE?

I JUST WANTED TO THROW IN MY RESIGNATION ALONG WITH THE REST.

YOU HAVEN'T SHOWN YOUR FACE HERE ALL *WEEK*. I ASSUMED YOU ALREADY HAD.

YOU ASSUMED RIGHT. I GUESS I WANTED TO MAKE IT *OFFICIAL*.

AND IF YOUR *FATHER* WAS HERE--

WHAT?

WHAT WOULD YOU *DO* IF MY FATHER *WAS* HERE?

I'D TELL HIM WHAT I'VE BEEN WANTING TO FOR *YEARS*.

I'D TELL HIM EVERYTHING MY MOTHER *BEGGED* ME *NOT* TO.

YOU KNOW WHAT, JORDAN? LET'S MAKE THIS DAY EVEN *BETTER* THAN IT *HAS* BEEN.

TELL *ME*.

YOUR FATHER PUT *MINE* IN A *DEATH TRAP!*

HE SAVED A FEW *BUCKS* AND HE SENT HIM OFF IN A PLANE THAT NEVER HAD A *CHANCE* AT *LANDING*.

AND NOW, WHILE *MY* DAD IS *ROTTING* IN THE *GROUND*, YOURS IS PLAYING *PUTT-PUTT* ON THE GULF OF THE MEXICO, DRINKING A MARGARITA AND PROBABLY SMOKING A CIGAR THAT COSTS MORE THAN WHAT I MAKE IN A DAY!

YOU DON'T MAKE *ANYTHING*, JORDAN. YOU JUST *QUIT*, REMEMBER?

NOW IS THAT *ALL* YOU'VE GOT TO *BARK* ABOUT?

FORGET IT, "LADY" FERRIS. I'LL SAVE THE REST FOR *HIM* WHEN HE'S *BACK* FROM HIS EXTENDED *HOLIDAY*.

DO YOU WANT TO FLY *AGAIN*?

WHAT?

DO YOU WANT TO FLY AGAIN?

YES.

BUT NOT *HERE.*

THEN *WHERE?*

WHO'S GOING TO HIRE YOU?

AFTER EVERYTHING YOU'VE DONE, *WHO'S* GOING TO TAKE THAT *RISK?*

I DIDN'T NEED A PLANE TO FLY ANYMORE.

THE RING MADE IT EASY.

THE RING MADE IT TOO EASY.

PLEASE, HAL.

I NEED A PILOT. AND YOU NEED A PLANE.

FOR A SPLIT SECOND, I DIDN'T SEE THE SHARK I THOUGHT SHE WAS. I SAW THE LITTLE GIRL I'D MET ALL THAT TIME AGO.

SHE CRIED LOUDER THAN I DID WHEN MY FATHER'S PLANE CRASHED.

SOMEHOW I'D FORGOTTEN THAT.

IT FELT GOOD TO FLY.

BUT IN THE BACK OF MY HEAD, I KNEW I WAS FLYING FOR THE WRONG PERSON.

I CONVINCED MYSELF I WAS ONLY STAYING UNTIL CARL FERRIS CAME BACK.

UNTIL I FINALLY GOT AN ANSWER TO THE QUESTION I'VE ASKED MYSELF A MILLION TIMES OVER.

HOW COULD HE LIVE THE WAY HE DOES AFTER WHAT HAPPENED?

HOW COULD HE SHIRK THE RESPONSIBILITY?

I TRIED TO STAY ANGRY IN THE AIR, BUT IT WAS HARD.

THE OPEN SKY INVITING ME BACK IN. AND CAROL FERRIS...

...WHY COULDN'T I STOP THINKING ABOUT HER?

CAROL.

FERRIS WANTS THIS ONE PRECISE, JORDAN. WE'RE ABOUT ROBUST TRAJECTORY TRACKING TODAY, NOT SPLIT-S MANEUVERS.

I WAS JUST LOOSENING UP.

WHAT HAPPENED TO THAT GIRL?

I DON'T KNOW IF THIS IS SUCH A GOOD IDEA, MISS FERRIS.

HE'S WANDERING ALL OVER THE PLACE. IF HE STARTS SOME OF HIS HOTDOGGING--

THIS IS HIS LAST CHANCE.

HE CAN'T SCREW IT UP.

VROOOM

WHAT IS THAT IMBECILE DOING?

FLYING WITHOUT HIS POWER RING.

WITHOUT HIS...? RING. LOCATE HIS POWER RING.

"THIS MAVERICK NEEDS A LESSON IN RESPONSIBILITY.

"BRING HIS RING TO ME."

WHOA!

HEY. I'VE GOT SOMETHING AT TWELVE O'CLOCK. THOUGHT I WAS ALONE UP HERE.

NOTHING ON OUR SCREEN. ARE YOU SURE?

VEEP VEEP VEEP

JORDAN?

COME IN, JORDAN.

BOOM

WHAT ARE YOU DOING?! *WHO ARE YOU?*

I AM SINESTRO.

GREEN LANTERN OF *SECTOR 1417.*

IS THAT SUPPOSED TO *IMPRESS* ME?

I WOULDN'T REMEMBER UNTIL LATER, "SINESTRO" WAS ABIN SUR'S LAST WORD.

I NEVER THOUGHT IT WAS A NAME.

Hr.

RING?

SECTOR 1417. THE MOST ORDERLY SECTOR IN ALL THE UNIVERSE.

AND I AM THE *GREATEST* GREEN LANTERN.

WHAT HAPPENED UP THERE?

WE DON'T KNOW, MISS FERRIS.

HE JUST *DISAPPEARED.* AND WE CAN'T MAKE *CONTACT.*

OUR DUTY AS GREEN LANTERNS EXTENDS FAR BEYOND *QUELLING* ANY EXTRATERRESTRIAL CRIMES WITHIN OUR SECTOR.

THE UNIVERSE IS RAMPANT WITH *CHAOS.*

IT IS OUR DUTY TO TURN THAT CHAOS INTO *ORDER*--

--AND *MAINTAIN* IT.

HOW DID YOU...?

I NEED TO GO.

GO? GO WHERE?

BACK TO MY *REAL* JOB.

YOU NEED MORE *TRAINING,* ROOKIE.

WHAT ARE YOU DOING HERE *ANYWAY?* TOMAR-RE TOLD ME ALL OF US ARE SUPPOSED TO STAY IN OUR *OWN* SECTOR.

YES, THE GUARDIANS' TERRITORIAL EDICT DISSUADES FRATERNIZING AMONG THE CORPS.

BUT I HAVE MY ORDERS. AND THEY ARE FROM A MUCH *HIGHER* AUTHORITY THAN TOMAR-RE.

I'VE BEEN DISPATCHED TO THIS PRIMITIVE PLANET PLAGUED WITH POLITICAL BORDERS AND TERRESTRIAL WAR TO INVESTIGATE THE DEATH OF YOUR PREDECESSOR.

ABIN SUR CRASHED HIS SHIP IN THE CALIFORNIA DESERT.

WHY?

I DON'T KNOW. HE DIDN'T TELL--

GREEN LANTERN OF SPACE SECTOR 1417--MESSAGE FROM GREEN LANTERN 2814 WAITING.

WHAT? WHAT DID YOUR RING SAY?

I DON'T KNOW. MAYBE YOURS IS SCREWING WITH IT.

MESSAGE WAITING.

STAY OUT OF MY FLIGHT PATH, SINESTRO.

I DON'T BELIEVE IT.

WHAT?

LOOK.

EEERRRTT

OH, BOY.

IT'S NOT WHAT IT LOOKS LIKE.

WHAT WAS *THAT*?

IT LOOKS LIKE YOU'RE PLAYING *GAMES*, MR. JORDAN.

PURPOSELY FLYING BELOW RADAR, REFUSING TO COMMUNICATE.

CAROL--

I MUST'VE BEEN *CRAZY* TO THINK THIS WAS A GOOD IDEA.

YOU'RE NOT *INSANE*, CAROL.

COAST CITY.

HAND MORTUARY ▽ ROOM 5

WILLIAM.

YOUR FATHER JUST FINISHED CLEANING THIS ONE UP!

I WASN'T D-D-DOING ANYTHING, MOM! I SWEAR!

HOW MANY TIMES HAVE WE TOLD YOU TO STAY *OUT* OF THE BASEMENT?

I KNOW, BUT...I JUST WANTED TO L-L-LOOK.

WHY? WHY CAN'T YOU BE A *GOOD CHRISTIAN* LIKE YOUR *BROTHERS?*

I DON'T KNOW.

YOU HAVE MET *EXTRA-TERRESTRIALS.*

LIFE FAR *BEYOND* OURS.

THEY GAVE YOU A *POWER RING.* A BAND OF *ENERGY* AND *WILL.*

THEY CALLED IT THE GREATEST *WEAPON* IN THE UNIVERSE.

THE GREATEST *TECHNOLOGY.*

HA HA HA HA HA!

GIVE ME THIS *EMERALD MIRACLE,* HAL JORDAN. GIVE...

...NO.

NO, YOU CAN'T HAVE *HER.*

NO, *CAROL FERRIS* IS MINE.

CHRISTINE FERRIS
Loving Wife and Mother

SHE'S *MINE!*

I DON'T... *WANT* HER, HAMMOND.

-- WAS BLIND HIM.

AAAAAAHHH!

CAROL?

YOUR BOYFRIEND'S BACK.

H-HAL?

HAL, WHAT'S GOING ON?

HE'S *NOT* MY BOYFRIEND.

LOOK AT THAT SHARED *TRAUMA.*

ALL THE *TRAGEDY* IN YOUR LIFE, IT'S NO WONDER YOU'RE *BOTH SO COLD.*

BUT *YOU* DON'T HAVE TO BE, CAROL. IT'S *YOUR* CHOICE.

YOU ARE ALSO BREAKING THIRTY-FOUR TERRESTRIAL AND INTERGALACTIC LAWS. CHIEF AMONG THEM, HUMAN, IS ATTACKING AN OFFICER OF THE GREEN LANTERN CORPS.

EVEN IF I DO USE THE TERM *"OFFICER"* LOOSELY.

WHAT?

RING. *REMOVE* HIS AIR SUPPLY.

APPROXIMATELY FIVE SECONDS UNTIL THE AIR FROM HIS LUNGS IS EVACUATED.

N-NO. WHO...?

THREE.

ONE.

ASTONISHING.

A RUDIMENTARY TELEPATH LIKE THAT ACTUALLY *DISRUPTED* YOUR CONCENTRATION?

GREEN... LANTERN?

COME, ROOKIE.

WOOOSHH

...HAL?

YOU WILL CONTAIN THIS POWER OF THE BLACK FOR MY JOURNEY *HOME.*

NOW TAKE ME TO ITS HOST.

KRIK

TAKE ME TO *WILLIAM* HAND.

KRIK
KRIK
KRIK
KRIK

...*REMOVING* THE AIR FROM HIS *LUNGS* WAS A *SIMPLE* SOLUTION. WITHOUT IT, HIS TELEKINETIC BRAIN HAD NO *CHOICE* BUT TO SHUT *DOWN*.

I WOULD'VE THOUGHT OF THAT.

I DON'T THINK YOU THINK OF *ANYTHING*, JORDAN. DO YOU *EVER* PLAN *AHEAD*?

FOR EXAMPLE: *FLYING* TODAY.

IF I HAD NOT BROUGHT YOU YOUR RING, YOU WOULD HAVE *DIED*.

AND YOU WOULD'VE BEEN A *MURDERER*. YOU WERE THE ONE IN MY *FLIGHT PATH*.

WHY WOULD YOU EVEN FLY *WITHOUT* YOUR RING?

SOMEHOW, I DOUBT THAT.

I FORGOT IT.

FINE. LESSON *LEARNED*. CAN YOU *GO* NOW? I'VE HAD ALL THE *TRAINING* I NEED.

KILOWOG TAUGHT ME HOW TO RING SLING.

POORLY.

SALAAK HAD ME TEST THE CHARGING LIMITATIONS.

SALAAK'S *"TESTS"* ARE WORTHLESS WHEN FACED WITH THE *REALITY* OF A *"DEAD"* RING.

AND *EVERYONE* WARNED ME ABOUT THE YELLOW IMPURITY.

OF COURSE, NO ONE CAN ACTUALLY TELL ME *WHAT* THAT IS OR *WHY* IT'S THERE.

IT DOESN'T EVEN MAKE ANY SENSE.

YELLOW.

Hh.

WHAT?

I HAVE BEEN ATTEMPTING TO SEEK THE TRUTH ABOUT THE YELLOW IMPURITY FOR YEARS. I WAS SUSPENDED AFTER ACCUSING THE GUARDIANS OF PUTTING IT THERE THEMSELVES WHEN *I* WAS A ROOKIE.

DID YOU KNOW HIM?

ABIN SUR WAS *MY* MENTOR.

I SUPPOSE I QUESTIONED HIM AND DISRESPECTED HIM AS MUCH AS YOU DO ME.

HE SHOWED ME HOW TO TEMPER THAT. AND WHY IT WAS NECESSARY FOR A MEMBER OF THE GREEN LANTERN CORPS.

SO HE TOLD YOU TO SHUT UP AND PLAY GOOD SOLDIER?

OF COURSE NOT. I AM AN INDIVIDUALISTIC THINKER, AS YOU ARE. I'D NEVER BELONGED TO A GROUP LIKE THE CORPS BEFORE.

SO I HAD NEVER LEARNED HOW TO *TRUST* THE BEINGS AROUND ME.

IN PART, THAT'S WHERE MY QUESTIONING CAME FROM.

HE HELPED ME LEARN TO TRUST MY FELLOW CORPSMAN. THANKFULLY, IT DIDN'T CHANGE MY DRIVE TO SEEK THE TRUTH OR MY DETERMINATION TO ARGUE AGAINST THE THEOLOGIES I DISAGREE WITH.

THEN WHAT *DID* IT HELP YOU DO, SINESTRO?

SINESTRO. GREEN LANTERN 1417 REGISTERED IN DIRECT VICINITY. MESSAGE 22 UNLOCKED.

I REALIZE I HAVE NOT BEEN AS RIGHTEOUS AND EFFECTIVE AN OFFICER LIKE YOU OF LATE.

BUT THIS TEACHER FEARS **NOT** BEING SURPASSED BY HIS STUDENT.

YOUR SUCCESS IS ALL I HOPE FOR, SINESTRO.

I HAVE LEARNED THE **SECRETS** OF LIFE.

AND TO UNDERSTAND THE SEVERITY OF MY MISSION IS TO UNDERSTAND THE GREATEST **TRAGEDY** THAT HAS EVER BEFALLEN THE UNIVERSE.

A CRIME SO HORRENDOUS AND UNFATHOMABLE, IT IS MYTH.

LONG BEFORE THE GUARDIANS OF THE UNIVERSE RECRUITED SENTIENT LIFE FORMS INTO THE GREEN LANTERN CORPS, THEY CREATED A DIFFERENT POLICE FORCE.

ONE THEY BELIEVED WOULD NEVER BE MANIPULATED BY EMOTION. THE GUARDIANS SAW EMOTION AS A WEAKNESS IN INTELLIGENT LIFE.

THEY CONSTRUCTED THOUSANDS OF ARTIFICIAL SOLDIERS. MANHUNTERS. THEY DISPATCHED THEM ACROSS THE UNIVERSE TO MAINTAIN ORDER.

FOR EONS, THEY DID JUST THAT.

UNTIL THE MASSACRE.

"THE MASSACRE OF SECTOR 666.

"IT HAPPENED IN AN **INSTANT**. A **GLITCH** WAS TRIGGERED, ACCIDENTALLY OR WITH PURPOSE, WITHIN THE MANHUNTERS.

"THEY CAME TO THE CONCLUSION THAT THERE COULD ONLY BE ORDER IN OUR UNIVERSE IF **LIFE** WERE ERADICATED.

"THEY ANNIHILATED WORLD AFTER WORLD. TRILLIONS OF INTELLIGENT BEINGS.

"THERE WERE **FIVE** SURVIVORS.

"**FIVE** WITHIN AN ENTIRE SECTOR ONCE FULL OF LIFE."

THOSE FIVE BECAME KNOWN AS THE **FIVE INVERSIONS**. A TERRORIST CELL BENT ON THE DESTRUCTION OF THE GUARDIANS OF THE UNIVERSE.

CHIEF AMONG THEM, **ATROCITUS**.

ALONG WITH QULL, THEY SOUGHT THE **INNER POWERS** OF THE UNIVERSE. WITH THEIR RITUALS AND SACRIFICES, THEY PEERED INTO THE DEEPEST **DEPTHS** OF THE FUTURE.

AND THEY SAW **DARKNESS**.

A **BLACK** SO **DEVOID** OF LIFE, EVEN THE GUARDIANS' **LIGHT** COULD NOT PENETRATE IT.

THEY SEEK TO TAKE THIS **DARKNESS** FOR THEMSELVES AND TURN IT AGAINST US.

IT WAS FORETOLD, THAT POWER WOULD BE FOUND ON EARTH. I KNOW YOU DO NOT BELIEVE THESE PROPHECIES, SINESTRO, NOR DO THE GUARDIANS. BUT I ASK, IN THE NAME OF OUR FRIENDSHIP, **TRUST ME.**

YOU MUST STOP THEM FROM UNLEASHING THIS DARKNESS.

IT WILL **DESTROY** THE UNIVERSE.

HE LOOKED... **SCARED**--

WHAT?

WHEN YOU SPOKE TO ABIN SUR, DID YOU SEE ANOTHER BODY?

ANOTHER **BODY**, JORDAN?

ABIN SUR WAS THE ONLY ONE I SAW IN THE SHIP. BUT HE WAS TORE UP PRETTY BAD. I THOUGHT IT WAS FROM THE CRASH. I DIDN'T THINK IT WAS BY **SOMEBODY**.

IT **WAS.**

ATROCITUS **SURVIVED.**

"WE NEED TO *FIND* HIM."

VISITING HOURS
3:30pm
5:30pm

KRIK

KRIK KRIK KRIK
KRIK KRIK KRIK

WILLIAM HAND.

KRIK KRIK
KRIK KRIK
KRIK KRIK

YOUR INSIDES HOLD THE DOORWAY TO ABSOLUTE DARKNESS.

ATROCITUS!

FEEL MY RAGE.

KID! GET OUT OF HERE!

RUN!

NNGGFF!

WARNING. POWER LEVELS DEPLETING.

POWER LEVELS AT 38.7%

SINESTRO? WHAT'S... HAPPENING?

HE'S BUILT A COSMIC DIVINING ROD.

IT CAN LOCATE POWER--

--AND IT CAN TAKE IT.

WARNING. POWER LEVELS APPROACHING 0.0%

GET ON YOUR FEET, JORDAN.

ONE ELSE HAD TO WATCH EIR FATHER DIE IN FRONT THEIR EYES.

THAT'S WHAT I THOUGHT MOST OF MY LIFE.

I THOUGHT I WAS ALONE.

GROWING UP, THE PILOTS WHO KNEW DAD WOULD LOOK AT ME WITH PITY WHEN I'D BEG TO GO ON A FLIGHT.

THEY ALWAYS REFUSED.

WHEN I FLEW MYSELF, THEY WOULD LOOK AT ME WITH ANNOYANCE. THINKING I WAS BREAKING THE RULES AND PUSHING THE BOUNDARIES UNTIL THE RIVETS POPPED OFF MY WINGS OUT OF ARROGANCE.

NO ONE EVER LOOKED AT ME WITH ANY KIND OF UNDERSTANDING.

NO ONE KNEW WHY I WAS THE WAY I WAS.

NOT UNTIL I MET SINESTRO.

JORDAN, FALL BACK.

I'VE NEVER RUN FROM A FIGHT BEFORE, SINESTRO. NOT GONNA START NOW.

YOUR RING IS EMPTY, LANTERN.

YOU ARE NOTHING TO ME.

SSLLAASSHH

GIVE ME YOUR BEST--

"FALLING BACK" IS A *MILITARY TACTIC*, JORDAN.

IT IS *NOT* A SIGN OF *FEAR*.

STANDING IN THE *LINE OF FIRE* WITH A *DRAINED* POWER RING, HOWEVER, IS A SIGN OF *STUPIDITY*.

YOU SHOULD BE *DEAD*.

YOU'RE NOT THE *FIRST* ONE TO TELL ME THAT.

I'M *SHOCKED*. THAT DEVICE ATROCITUS IS HOLDING IS CAPABLE OF *REMOVING* AND *CONTAINING* THE ENERGY WITHIN OUR RINGS.

WE NEED TO KEEP *CLEAR* OF IT AND WE NEED TO *RECHARGE*.

WHAT ARE YOU DOING?

RECALLING MY *POWER BATTERY*.

DON'T TELL ME SALAAK DIDN'T EDUCATE YOU ON CONFINED POCKET DIMENSIONS AND THE STORAGE OF PERSONAL CHARGING UNITS.

I KEEP MINE IN MY LOCKER.

YOU'VE REDEFINED THE WORD *CARELESS* FOR ME, JORDAN.

SO I TAUGHT *YOU* SOMETHING?

JUST *LIGHT UP*, ROOKIE.

COME **ON**, JORDAN! STOP WITH THE **HANDS** AND **FORCE SPHERES**.

OPEN UP YOUR **MIND**.

AND **STRENGTHEN** THOSE **CONSTRUCTS**.

LET **GO** OF YOUR **ANGER**!

A **ROOKIE**.

BUT **YOU**...

...I **KNOW** **YOU**, LANTERN.

YOU ARE **SINESTRO**.

OUR PROPHECIES SAY YOU ARE THE **GREATEST** OF THEM ALL.

THEY SAY IF **ANYONE** IS TO OPPOSE OUR **REVENGE**, IT IS **YOU**.

Nn...

BUT THEY ALSO SAY YOU HAVE A **WEAKNESS**.

LIKE **ALL** OF THE GUARDIANS' TERRORISTS.

I WILL BATHE IN YOUR BLOOD, "GREAT ONE."

NO!

YELLOW...?

...THAT WAS... NOT POSSIBLE...

YOU KNOW MY NAME, ATROCITUS?

GOOD.

TELL THE OTHER *FOUR* OF THE *INVERSIONS* WHO THEY HAVE TO *FEAR*.

GHOOOMMM

SINESTRO. THE *GREATEST* GREEN LANTERN OF THEM *ALL*.

HEY!

HEY, KID! YOU ALL RIGHT?

HEY--!

LET THE BOY GO, JORDAN.

WHAT DID ATROCITUS WANT WITH HIM?

THEY GAIN POWER THROUGH THE BLOOD OF OTHERS THEY DEEM "DOORWAYS." BEINGS THEY BELIEVE ARE TIED TO THE GREATER FABRIC OF UNIVERSAL POWER.

UTTER NONSENSE.

YOU SAW WHAT I DID, DIDN'T YOU? WHAT DID YOU DO?

I USED THE RING AGAINST YELLOW.

YOU ASSISTED IN THIS TAKEDOWN AND ARREST, JORDAN, WITHOUT YOUR RING SEEKING A REPLACEMENT.

YOU SURVIVED. THAT'S ENOUGH.

YOU DON'T BELIEVE ME?

YOU DON'T THINK I'VE TRIED TO PIERCE THE SPECTRUM BARRIER? IT IS *FUTILE*. EVEN FOR *ME*.

I *DID*.

ENOUGH.

#$%& YOU.

UNABLE TO TRANSLATE.

HFFF. YOU HAVE TO STAND OUT, DON'T YOU?

YOU CAN'T STAND TO BE *UPSTAGED*?

BEING A MEMBER OF THE CORPS, YOU'LL NEED TO GET *USED* TO IT.

WHAT MAKES ANYONE THINK I *WANT* TO BE AFTER ALL THIS?

YOU NEED TO GET HOLD OF YOUR *ANGER*, JORDAN. THAT'S WHAT ALMOST GOT YOU *KILLED* TODAY.

I DON'T KNOW *WHAT* OR *WHO* YOU'RE SO *ANGRY* WITH, BUT YOU CONTINUE TO DIRECT IT AT *ME*.

YOU NEED TO *GROW UP*, *DEAL* WITH IT AND GET *ON* WITH YOUR *LIFE*.

YOU KNOW WHAT? I WILL.

RING. TAKE ME TO *CARL FERRIS*.

JORDAN? JORDAN?!

WE HAVE PROTOCOLS TO FOLLOW!

I DIDN'T LIKE SINESTRO. BUT HE WAS RIGHT. ALL THAT ANGER WASN'T ABOUT HIM.

I THOUGHT IT'D TAKE ME TO A BEACH HOUSE IN FLORIDA...

...INSTEAD I FOUND MYSELF FLYING DOWN TO HIS HOUSE OUTSIDE COAST CITY.

BUMMBUMM BUMM

BUMMBUMM BUMM

JORDAN?

WHAT ARE YOU DOING HERE?

WHERE IS HE, CAROL?

WHO?

YOUR FATHER.

WHERE IS THE OLD MAN?

HE'S NOT--

HE'S HERE.

I KNOW HE IS.

AND I'M GOING TO SEE HIM.

JORDAN, WAIT!

WHERE IS HE?

PLEASE, STOP.

FERRIS--?!

WHAT...

...WHAT IS THIS?

HE'S SICK.

YOUR FATHER WAS HIS **BEST FRIEND.** AND AFTER THE CRASH...

...IT **TORE** HIM UP INSIDE. AND OVER THE YEARS, THE **GUILT** TOOK ITS TOLL.

HE WAS NEVER GOLFING ON PEBBLE BEACH?

HE'S NEVER PLAYED GOLF IN HIS LIFE. LAST YEAR, WHEN HE GOT TOO SICK TO GET OUT OF BED, FERRIS AIR WAS ALREADY IN TROUBLE.

SO YOU STOPPED FLYING? YOU STARTED RUNNING FERRIS? AND YOU LET EVERYONE THINK YOUR FATHER WAS DOING IT ALL THROUGH **YOU?**

I DIDN'T KNOW WHAT ELSE TO DO.

THAT COMPANY. AFTER MOM AND YOUR FATHER, IT'S ALL **HE** HAD **LEFT.**

HE STILL HAS **YOU.**

I WAS A **SPOILED BRAT.**

WHEN MOM DIED, HE'D GIVE ME ANYTHING I WANTED AS LONG AS I SCREAMED **LOUD** ENOUGH.

ONE DAY, HE **REFUSED.** I DON'T EVEN KNOW WHAT I WAS AFTER, BUT I REMEMBER I SAID...

...I SAID I WISHED **MOM** WAS THERE INSTEAD OF **HIM.**

HE SAW YOU BRING YOUR DAD A BROWN BAG LUNCH AND HE TOLD ME...

...HE WISHED HE HAD A SON LIKE **YOU.**

HE WOULDN'T IF HE **KNEW** ME.

YOU'RE **HERE** FOR HIM. ME?

I'VE **NEVER** BEEN THERE FOR **ANYONE** IN MY FAMILY.

ALL THESE YEARS. ALL THIS *TIME.* AND I'VE *WASTED* IT.

I'VE WASTED IT *HATING* SOMEONE. BEING *ANGRY* AT SOMEONE.

SOMEONE WHO *DESERVE* IT.

A *LOT* OF PEOPLE WHO DIDN'T DESERVE IT.

I'M *SORRY,* CAROL.

I'M *SO* SORRY.

YOU'VE JUST WITNESSED THE *TRUE* POWER OF THE RING.

IT HAS HELPED YOU FIND THE *WILL* TO *LIVE.*

IT IS THE MOST *BASIC* ELEMENT WITHIN ONE'S WILLPOWER.

YOU WERE RIGHT.

I KNOW.

YOU AREN'T RIGHT ABOUT *EVERYTHING.*

BUT THE ANGER... THE ANGER I'VE HELD ONTO SINCE I WAS A *KID*...

...THAT'S BEEN FOR *NOTHING.* THAT HASN'T HELPED ANYONE.

BERATING YOU IS *MY* JOB, NOT *YOURS.*

I MYSELF HAVE SUFFERED LOSS, JORDAN. *GREAT* LOSS.

WITHOUT ABIN THERE TO HELP ME, I DOUBT THIS RING WOULD STILL BE *MINE.*

FOR BEINGS LIKE US, OVERCOMING FEAR IS WHAT WE DO BEST. BUT WHEN IT COMES TO GUILT, REGRET... *LOSS*...

...EVEN *GREEN LANTERNS* STRUGGLE WITH THOSE.

YOU ARE WELL AWARE OF THE *LIMITS* WE HAVE PUT ON THE CONGREGATION OF OUR OFFICERS *OFF* THE PLANET OA.

THESE ARE THE *GUARDIANS* OF THE *UNIVERSE?* THEY'RE SO *SMALL--*

SHUT UP.

THIS IS THE *SECOND TIME* YOU HAVE *DISOBEYED* US. AND *AGAIN* WITH THE GREEN LANTERN OF SECTOR 2814.

ALBEIT IT A *DIFFERENT* ONE. THIS IS NOT *ABIN SUR.*

MY NAME'S HAL JORDAN.

THEY *KNOW* THAT.

SINESTRO--?

EXPLAIN YOURSELF.

I WAS SIMPLY ASSISTING THIS OFFICER IN *LOCATING* AND *ARRESTING* THE *KILLER* WHO ENDED THE LIFE OF ABIN SUR.

ATROCITUS OF THE FIVE INVERSIONS.

AND BEFORE YOU SO *ARROGANTLY* RIPPED ME AWAY FROM THAT BACKWARDS BALL OF *DIRT*, I HAD HIM IN *CUSTODY*.

WE ARE WELL *AWARE*.

ATROCITUS WAS *TETHERED* TO YOUR RING.

THIS *TERRORIST* WILL BE RETURNED TO YSMAULT WHERE HE WILL CONTINUE HIS *SENTENCE*--

--AN *ETERNITY* OF IMPRISONMENT.

HOWEVER, THIS ARREST DOES NOT *EXCUSE YOU* FROM BREAKING OUR TERRITORIAL EDICT, SINESTRO.

GREEN LANTERNS MUST ONLY OPERATE IN THEIR *RESPECTIVE* SECTORS. THEY MUST PATROL *INDEPENDENTLY*. THEY MUST *FLY* ON THEIR OWN--

WHY?

WORKING INDEPENDENTLY WILL MAKE YOU *STRONGER,* HAL JORDAN OF EARTH.

YOU WILL *LEARN* THAT THE ENEMIES OF *ORDER* WILL STOP AT *NOTHING* TO SPREAD *CHAOS.*

DO NOT *QUESTION* THE GUARDIANS.

WHY?

WE HAVE LIVED FOR *BILLIONS* OF YEARS.

WHAT WE DO, WE DO FOR THE *WELL-BEING* OF THE *ENTIRE* UNIVERSE.

LIKE THE *MANHUNTERS?*

JORDAN--

THE ANDROIDS THAT DID OUR JOB BEFORE THEY WENT *"GLITCHY"* AND SLAUGHTERED *EVERY* LIVING BEING IN SECTOR 666 BUT THE FIVE INVERSIONS--?

THEY ARE *LIES* FROM ATROCITUS--

IT *WASN'T* ATROCITUS THAT TOLD US ABOUT THE *MASSACRE.* IT WAS *ABIN SUR.* A MESSAGE--

MORE FABLES TO INSTILL *FEAR* AMONG YOU.

INSTILL FEAR IN *US?* YOU KNOW WHAT *I* THINK?

I THINK *YOU'RE* AFRAID.

"AND THE *BUILDINGS* ON OA, THE CITADEL OF THE GUARDIANS, THEY ALL JUST *HAPPEN* TO BE *YELLOW?*"

"BECAUSE THEY'RE *AFRAID* WE'LL TURN ON THEM LIKE THEIR *ROBOTS* DID."

THEY EXPECT *US* TO OVERCOME OUR FEARS.

WHAT ABOUT WHAT THE *GUARDIANS* FEAR?

AND THAT *TERRITORIAL* EDICT?

THAT EDICT IS $#%?!$%#.

UNABLE TO TRANSLATE.

ENOUGH.

YOUR ACCUSATIONS AND DISRESPECT CAUSE US *GREAT* CONCERN.

YOU ARE ON THE VERGE OF *EXPULSION*, HAL JORDAN OF EARTH.

GUARDIANS.

YOU EXPEL JORDAN, YOU CAN HAVE *MY* RING AS WELL.

OA *HELP* ME, THE EARTHMAN IS *RIGHT*.

I AM?

QUIET. PLEASE.

WE *CAN* BE STRONGER *TOGETHER*.

THE CORPS *SHOULD* WORK IN UNISON WHEN NECESSARY.

AND IT SHOULD BE UP TO *US* TO NOT ONLY HELP OUR FELLOW OFFICERS *GROW*, BUT TO KEEP THEM IN *CHECK*. TO INSURE THAT THE TRAGEDY THAT HAPPENED IN SECTOR 666 *NEVER* HAPPENS AGAIN.

ALL OF *THIS*. THIS STARTED BECAUSE ONE OF YOU *SENT* ME TO ASSIST ABIN SUR'S REPLACEMENT.

ONE OF US?

THE ONE WHO CALLS HIMSELF "*GANTHET*."

"GANTHET"?

WE TAKE *NO* NAMES.

ONE OF YOU *HAS*.

WHICH ONE?

I BELIEVE WE HAVE HEARD *MUCH* TO CONSIDER, SINESTRO. FOR NOW, WE LEAVE THE EARTHMAN WITH HIS RING.

AND OBVIOUSLY, *YOU* WITH *YOURS*.

YES. BUT HE IS NOW AS MUCH *YOUR* RESPONSIBILITY AS KORUGAR AND THE REST OF SECTOR 1417.

WE *TRUST* THAT IS *ACCEPTABLE*, SINESTRO...

...*GREATEST* OF THE *GREEN LANTERNS*.

Hr.

YES.

"THAT IS ACCEPTABLE."

HNNN!!

FSSSSSSS

I DID DO IT.

YOU DIDN'T DO IT.

I DID.

NO ONE CAN BREAK THROUGH YELLOW, JORDAN. NOT EVEN SINESTRO.

I CAN--

YOU ONLY TRIED LIKE TWENTY TIMES, HUMAN! YOU CAN TRY ANOTHER THOUSAND AND IT WON'T MAKE A DIFFERENCE.

I BELIEVE HIM.

YOU, TOMAR-RE? YOU ALWAYS HAD FAITH FAR TOO READILY.

I SUPPOSE THAT IS ONE THING ABIN TAUGHT ME THAT HE NEVER TAUGHT YOU.

I SUPPOSE...

...I MUST GO.

I DO NOT HAVE TIME FOR ANY MORE GAMES...

...THE GUARDIANS HAVE BOTHERED ME WITH THE *TASK* OF RETURNING ATROCITUS TO YSMAULT.

SINESTRO.

IF YOU'RE GOING TO SAY ANYTHING, JORDAN, SAY "I WON'T MAKE YOU *REGRET* THIS."

I WON'T.

THAT IS ALL I NEED TO HEAR, BECAUSE, *UNFORTUNATELY,* A "GOODBYE" IS NOT APPROPRIATE.

WE WILL RECONVENE IN ONE MONTH SO THAT I MAY EVALUATE YOUR PROGRESS.

BUT *NEXT* TIME--

--YOU'RE COMING TO *MY* WORLD.

"FERRIS IS LETTING *YOU* FLY?"

"IT'S NOT LIKE SHE HAD MUCH OF A CHOICE, TOM."

I GUESS NOT.

BUT BEING THE ONLY PILOT--

FOR NOW.

BEING THE ONLY PILOT, YOU'RE GOING TO BE LOGGING A HECKUVA LOT OF *FLIGHT TIME.*

THAT'S WHAT I'M HOPING.

I STILL DON'T GET WHY YOU WANT TO FLY A *PLANE* WHEN YOU'VE GOT THAT *MAGIC RING.*

THE RING'S NOT *MAGIC.* THE PLANES ARE.

SPEAKING OF. WHICH ONE AM I TAKING UP TODAY?

THAT ONE OVER THERE.

FWUMP

THIS IS...THIS IS THAT HUNK OF JUNK. THIS IS THE PLANE MY DAD FLEW ME IN. BUT--

I'M GOOD, *huh?* ONLY TOOK ME THREE WEEKS.

IT'S AMAZING, TOM.

IT SEEMED LIKE SHE MEANT A LOT TO YOU. I TOLD MISS FERRIS. SHE SAID I COULD FIX IT UP.

CAROL *DID?*

WHEN EVERY OTHER PILOT *LEFT,* I NEEDED *SOMETHING* TO KEEP YOU HERE.

ANYTHING SPECIAL PLANNED TONIGHT?

HEADING DOWN TO PANCHO'S WITH THE GUYS. MY GIRLFRIEND'S BEEN A PAIN LATELY. SHE'S BEEN ON MY CASE ABOUT THE "NEXT LEVEL" OF OUR RELATIONSHIP.

I TOLD HER THE NEXT LEVEL IS ME MOVIN' ON OUT!

I HAVE A GIRLFRIEND TOO.

DO YOU HEAR ME?

HELLO?

ANYONE? DO YOU HEAR ME?

YOU CAN'T LEAVE ME IN HERE. THIS IS A TERRIBLY EMPTY PLACE! A VILE PLACE!

I'M NOT LIKE THAT ALIEN SHIP! I'M NOT HERE TO BE POKED AND PRODDED!

DON'T LISTEN TO THE GREEN LANTERN!

HE IS AMAZING THOUGH. THE LIFE HE LIVES IS SO THRILLING.

THE LEAPS AND THE FLIGHTS AND THE WOMEN.

YES.

I WANT TO BE A PART OF THAT EXCITEMENT. OH, IT'LL BE WONDERFUL WHEN I AM AGAIN!

YES, OH, YES!

I'M FEELING BETTER ALREADY.

...REPORTS OF MORE **STRANGE LIGHTS** IN THE SKY ARE POURING IN.

COAST CITY HOSPITAL
C C H

U.F.O.'S? SECRET AIR FORCE TEST FLIGHTS? OR ARE THESE RUMORS OF A GLOWING GREEN **MAN** TRUE?

IS THE **GREEN LANTERN** REAL?

WITH THE RECENT APPEARANCE OF **SUPERMAN** IN METROPOLIS, COULD COAST CITY HAVE ITS VERY OWN PROTECTOR? AN EMERALD WARRIOR--?

KLANK

KLK

CHRIST.

I D-D-DIDN'T DO ANYTHING **WRONG.**

STAND **UP.** STAND UP AND GET AWAY FROM THAT--

SWAPEE!

FWASSSSH

IT'S OKAY. DEAD IS G-G-GOOD.

DEAD IS **GOOD.**

YSMAULT.

BY ORDER OF THE GUARDIANS, I RETURN YOU TO YOUR CRUCIFIX, ATROCITUS.

YOU ARE TO SERVE OUT THE REMAINDER OF YOUR SENTENCE FOR YOUR CRIMES.

NNYYAAA!

FAREWELL, FELON.

WE WITNESSED THE *FATE* OF ABIN SUR, SINESTRO!

WE CAN SEE *ANOTHER!*

YOUR *TALES* WILL NOT *FRIGHTEN* ME, QULL. I CAN LOOK OUT FOR MYSELF.

QULL IS NOT SPEAKING OF *YOU*, SINESTRO. I SEE IT NOW *TOO*.

AS DO I.

KORUGAR.

HAL?

JIM?

JACK'S NOT COMING.

I'M SORRY.

I DIDN'T THINK HE WOULD.

I DON'T *BLAME* HIM. I WOULDN'T HAVE BLAMED YOU *EITHER.*

I'VE *NEVER* BEEN A GOOD *BROTHER.*

THE END